carly Hatton

Limericks
from the
Animal Kingdom

Spiral Press,
R.R. 5, Rockwood, ON N0B 2K0
www.spiralpress.ca

Spiral Press Logo
by Ken Coward, Holy Cow Communication Design Inc.
 www.holycowcom.com

Photo of Carly Hatton by Alberta Nye
Photo of Mary Hackney from Hackney Family Archives

ISBN 978-0-9867912-1-5

10 9 8 7 6 5 4 3 2 1

Limericks
from the
Animal Kingdom

by I. Mary Hackney

Illustrations by Carly Hatton

Spiral
Press

A portion of the proceeds from
Limericks from the Animal Kingdom
goes to the Hackney-Hatton Fund
to support families of children living with autism.

Table of Contents

1. Fraud Squad
2. Lounge Lizard
3. Sea Saw
4. Savile Row
5. Tour for Two
6. Evil Knievel
7. Culture Vulture
8. Dammit
9. Basic Literacy
10. Back Pack
11. 2 x 2 x 2
12. Wotta Schnozzle
13. Zing Zong
14. Hum Drum
15. Razzberry
16. Robber Baron
17. Camouflage
18. Moby Dick
19. Lese Majesté
20. Goosey Goosey Gander
21. Women's Rights
22. Boarding House Reach
23. Duvet
24. The Snob

25. Marx Larx

26. Fool's Gold

27. Misplaced

28. White Night

29. Under the Table

30. Gourmand

31. Mistaken Identity

32. Good Grief

33. Bump in the Night

34. Worm Turn

35. Slinky

36. End Game

37. Buzz Off

38. Fish Story

39. Phew

40. Ahem

41. Addition

42. Dot Dot Dash

43. Boss Bully

44. Smug Mug

45. Smack, Bang, Pop

46. Chitter, Chatter

47. Birdwatchers' Delight

48. Passive Resistence

49. How Does That Grab You?

50. Different Talents

51. Foster Care

52. Animal, Vegetable, or Mineral?

53. Zoo Blue

54. Ironical Moniker

55. Narcissist

56. Dirty Joke

57. Malnutrition

58. Big Bird

59. Bad Example

60. Doggo

61. Easy Does it

62. The Wanderer

63. Dude of the Wilds

64. Live and Learn

65. Rig a Jig Jig

66. Fun Fur

67. Cheese It, E.A.Poe

68. Woo Coo

69. Flip Trip

70. Loan Shark

71. Invidious Comparisons

72. Woo Woo

73. Tip Top

74. Die Fledermaus

75. Blubber

76. Christmas Travel

77. The Grizzly

78. Night Howl

79. It Makes Sense

80. What a Comedown

Limericks

from the

Animal Kingdom

1. Fraud Squad

The sparrow claims once on a time
That he killed cock robin, a crime
But the limerick maker
Knows he is a faker
For he only said it to rhyme.

2. Lounge Lizard

A well-meaning Everglades' gator
Got a job as a cocktail lounge waiter
But the day he was hired
He also got fired
For he picked up a bunny and ate her.

3. Sea Saw

A restless Galapagos iguana
Tired of tourists admiring the fauna
Went first to Moldavia
And then Scandinavia
Where it settled, enjoying the sauna.

4. Savile Row

The king penguin's suit is impressive
Of his dignity it is expressive
But his exquisite taste
Is a terrible waste
For Antarctica it seems excessive.

5. Tour for Two

The female great grey kangaroo
Warns her joey of journeys on cue
He leaps into her pocket
She takes off like a rocket
And soon they have reached pastures new.

6. Evil Knievel

The wolverine gets a bad press
Trashing traplines, leaving camps in a mess
But his very worst crime
Is that much of the time
He makes fools of men, more or less.

7. Culture Vulture

In spite of all claims, the black vulture
Has no avid interest in culture,
He wallows in gore
And comes back for more,
With no painting or music or sculpture.

8. Dammit

The beaver's a nocturnal rodent
And I ask what our founders had meant
In selecting this dingbat
A sizable water rat
As symbol of nation and government.

9. Basic Literacy

There's not very much in a gnu
He's been here for years, quite a few
There is really no telling
How he got his spelling
And is he a " new " or a " noo "?

10. Back Pack

In the far Himalayas, the yak,

Carries large loads of freight on its back,

And besides, it provides

Milk, meat, hair, and hides

In fact, with a yak, one can't lack.

II. 2 × 2 × 2

The cute little cottontail's habits
Are just as conforming as Babbitt's
He girdles our fruit trees
And chews up our garden peas
And multiplies almost like rabbits.

12. Wotta Schnozzle

The roar of the elephant seal
Says he'll make of his rivals a meal.
He guards his whole harem
And bellows to scare 'em
For the risk of male piracy's real.

13. Zing Zong

Cicadas hide high in the trees
Their song makes us long that they'd cease,
Their buzzing and zinging
Will start our ears ringing
If we caught 'em, we'd squinch' em, for peace.

14. Hum Drum

Among hummers, the ruby throat's best.
He travels long distance with zest.
While all of his cousins
Of whom there are dozens
Remain in the tropics and rest.

15. Razzberry

Approaching the dignified camel
Is really a bit of a gamble
If a man is close by
He may spit in his eye
He thinks man's an inferior mammal.

16. Robber Baron

The raccoon's bandit mask is quite handsome

But he holds Rosedale households to ransom

The attic and chimney

He enters so nimbly

Coming in any crevice or transom.

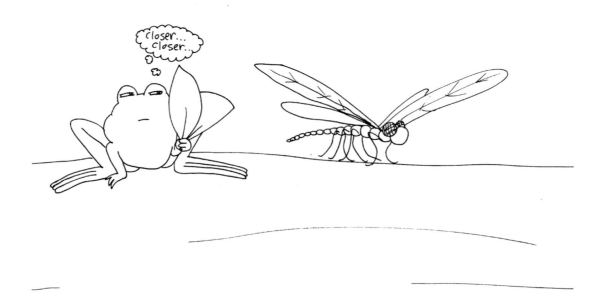

17. Camouflage

The humungous grandfather frog
Hides out in the depths of a bog
His favourite solution
To avoid persecution
Is to look like a bump on a log.

18. Moby Dick

When crossing the ocean the whale
Is safe in the teeth of a gale.
But everyone knows,
That the shout, "Thar she blows!"
Means there's really more teeth in a sail.

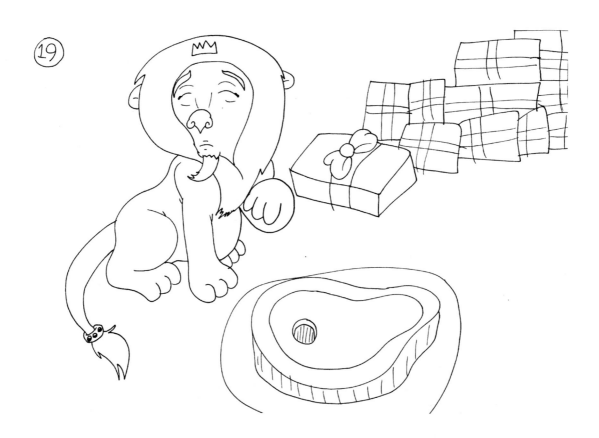

19. Lese Majesté

The lion, symbol of many a nation,
Is supposed to arouse admiration.
But the king of the beasts
Freeloads for his feasts
Which really implies exploitation.

20. Goosey Goosey Gander

The Canada goose is a bummer
When other birds, small as a hummer
Migrate back and forth
To the south and the north
He sticks around winter and summer.

21. Women's Rights

The lioness should not rely on
A fair deal or shoulder to cry on
When she hunts for the dinner
She's seldom the winner
The lion's share goes to the lion.

22. Boarding House Reach

Because of his greed, the giraffe
Has developed a neck and a half,
He's accustomed to munch on
A top of tree luncheon
And uses his tongue as a gaff.

23. Duvet

If the eider duck has any luck
He will duck to avoid being struck
By missiles that whistle
Through down of the thistle
Not as downy as down of the duck.

24. The Snob

The arrogant stare of the hawk
As he flies by on high, seems to mock
Inadequate earthlings
Who don't have his broad wings
To sail over prairie and rock.

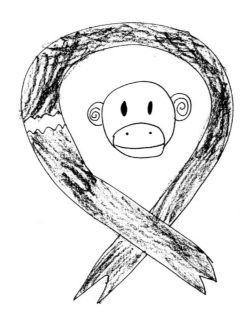

25. Marx Larx

My favourite ape is the gibbon
His accomplishments rate a blue ribbon
He's crazy and cute
Agile and astute
And he eats his duck soup with a bib on.

26. Fool's Gold

After lessons in English, the mynah
Tried to dig a deep hole down to China,
You see, he'd been told
That in digging for gold
In China, gold's dug by a mynah.

27. Misplaced

The woodchuck doesn't live in a wood
But he would chuck wood if he could
Living in clover
Is not bad, however,
He still would prefer to chuck wood.

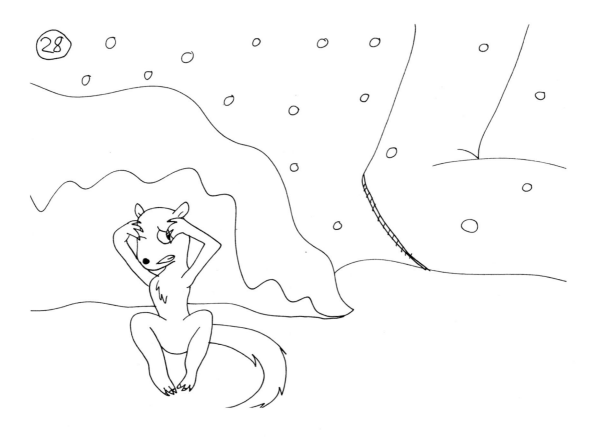

28. White Night

Among weasels, the ermine is kin,
But look at the fix he is in.
When the winter winds blow
And his fur's white as snow
He's in danger of losing his skin.

29. Under the Table

A beautiful fur has the sable
Adorning the knight in the fable
In the USSR
He should get a Red Star
And he will, when the sable is able.

30. Gourmand

A silverback mountain gorilla
Ate his leaves with a dash of vanilla
Since the flavour was bland
He persuaded his band
To switch over to sarsaparilla.

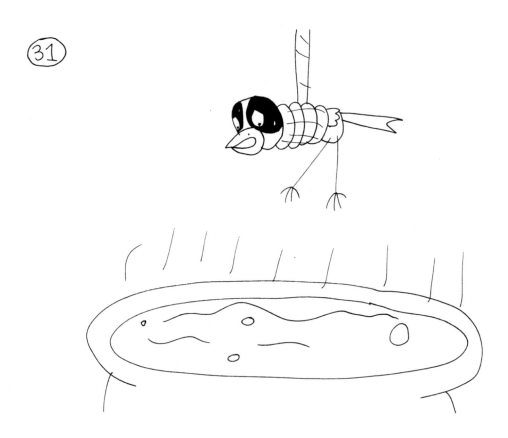

31. Mistaken Identity

A bouncy arboreal chickadee
Met his end in a soup pot in Chicopee
Though he was small
They thought nothing at all
Of putting the chick in their fricassee.

32. Good Grief

The shedding of crocodile tears
Has been seen as a symbol for years
Of the pretense of woe
That hypocrites show
While giving their victims the gears.

33. Bump in the Night

The hoots of the nocturnal owl
When the banshee's beginning to howl
Fill the Hallowe'en night
Give the children a fright
Cause the burglar to throw in the towel.

34. Worm Turn

The robin who hops on my lawn
Eats earthworms at lunch and at dawn
Then the poor little sinner
Puts up with a dinner
So boring a hippo would yawn.

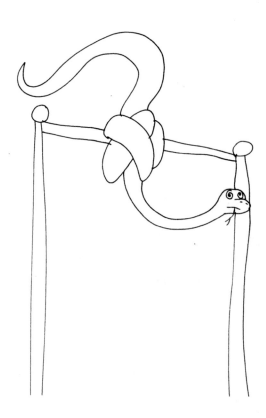

35. Slinky

A clever and spry anaconda
With no feet, but an itch to go yonda,
Set off for Hollywood
Thinking he likely could
Teach gymnastic stunts to Jane Fonda.

36. End Game

The strident remarks of the blue jay
Ring the welkin' at morn and at noonday
The fans watching baseball
In the Sky dome at nightfall
Hurl strident remarks _at_ the Blue Jay

---

[1] poetic term for the sky or heaven

37. Buzz Off

The busy and buzzy wild bee
Put his hive in a crotch of a tree
When the weather is sunny
The honey gets runny
And the bear climbs to have a look-see.

38. Fish Story

Among herons, the handsome great blue
Has a fishing technique that is new.
He stands on one foot
In the clear babbling brook
And pretends that he hasn't a clue.

39. Phew

So gentle and harmless the skunk
As virtuous as any monk
And as for beauty
He's really a cutie
We'd no right to complain when he stunk.

40. Ahem

The elephant will not permit
Making up limericks about it.
Its trunk and its tusk
Its hide and its musth[2]
Are no subjects for dubious wit.

---

[2]Variant spelling of must meaning the frenzied state of some male animals, esp. elephants and camels, at certain times

41. Addition

The wee sleakit[3] cowerin' mouse
Turns up without fail in my house
In the rains of November
And I know by December
She'll have brought in her children and spouse

---

[3] A Scottish word meaning sly or cunning

42. Dot Dot Dash

It's so difficult spotting the leopard
For with shadowy dots he is peppered.
His disguise is so wise
One cannot advise
The changing of spots of the leopard.

43. Boss Bully

The seagull's an expert on scrounging
He does it by waterfront lounging
There may be dead fish
To him, they're delish,
And he gets stuff by robbing and gouging.

44. Smug Mug

The panda's unbearably cute
On the other hand, also astute.
His facial expression,
Gives us the impression
That he's laughing at us, although mute.

45. Smack, Bang, Pop

The playful, bewhiskered sea otter
Has a skill taught by mother to daughter
To float on her back
With a rock there to crack
Shellfish she has brought to the slaughter.

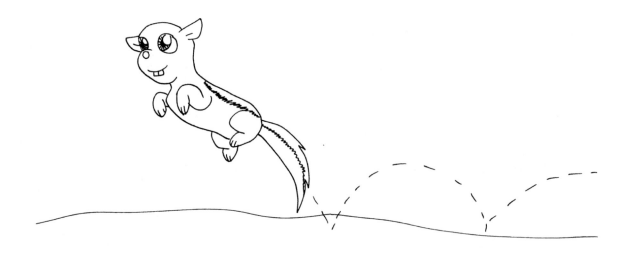

46. Chitter, Chatter

The chipmunk's a loveable pixie
From Canada right down to Dixie
    He rustles and chatters
    And scurries and natters
And makes enough racket for sixty.

47. Birdwatchers' Delight

At the seaside, invisible Peeps,
Race along giving faint little cheeps
Sandpipers so tiny
Can't be seen by the briny
Unless there are zillions and heaps.

48. Passive Resistance

Though the zebra does not go berserk
Like mustangs, who kick, buck and jerk,
Man has never been able
To put him in a stable
Or to get him to do any work.

49. How Does That Grab You?

The human race has to contrive
With two grasping hands to survive
The monkey can manage
With his great advantage
With his prehensile tail, he has five.

50. Different Talents

The woodpecker, joining the symphony,
Played rat-a-tat-tat in the tympany
He had no other choice
For his raucous voice
Made the symphony into cacophony.

51. Foster Care

Cowbirds, irresponsible rats,
Palm their eggs off on warblers and chats
Who never have guessed
With his eggs in their nests
They'll be bringing up bigger birds' brats.

52. Animal, Vegetable or Mineral?

A geologist based on the Niger
Spent his off-hours hunting for tiger
But he wasn't aware
There aren't tigers there
And you don't hunt for a tiger with a geiger.

53. Zoo Blue

A healthy East African hippo
Was sent to a zoo in Aleppo
His life mongst the Arabs
Wasn't all beer and scarabs
But he loved his kind keeper, named Beppo

54. Ironical Moniker

The stupendously massive white rhino
Isn't white, and it isn't albino.
Such misleading names
Cause much fun and games
From Antarctica up to Fort Chimo.

55. Narcissist

The proud peacock only displays
His magnificent tail on fine days
He puts to the test
He is looking his best
With the help of the sun's brightest rays.

56. Dirty Joke

The spotted hyena, they say
Laughs often by night, less by day
His habits are nasty
His manners are ghastly
So his humour is sick, and not gay.

57. Malnutrition

The flamingo knows every link
In the food chain, and when on the brink
Of going grey, he eats shrimp
Like a long legged blimp
And thereby he keeps in the pink.

58. Big Bird

The ostrich so stately and grand
Can plume himself on his command
Of a means of survival
With the sandstorm's arrival
By putting his head in the sand.

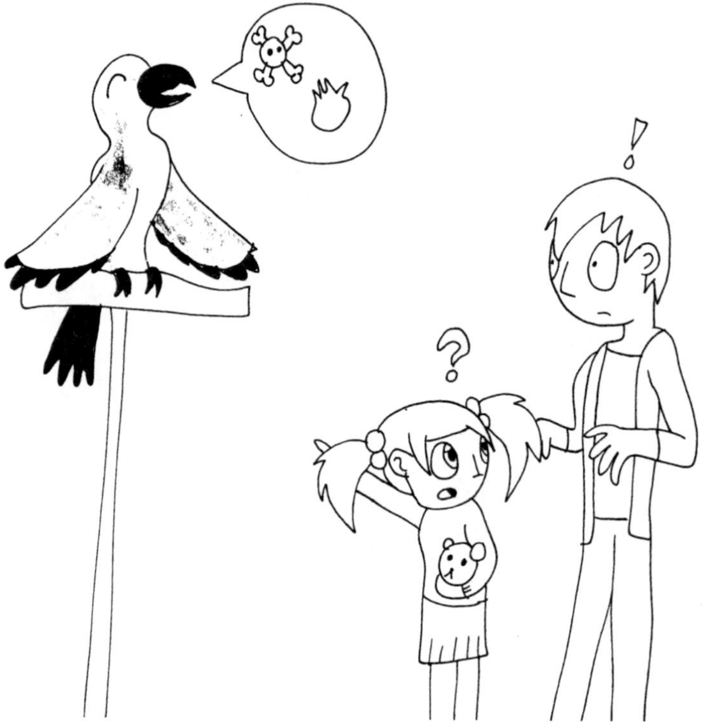

59. Bad Example

The parrot, green, yellow and red,
Is a mimic, or so it is said,
Has the doubtful ability
To repeat with facility
Remarks that are often ill-bred.

60. Doggo

The opossum is stupid, it's said,
But look at the way he has spread
And one of his ways,
To lengthen his days
Is playing' possum, pretending he's dead.

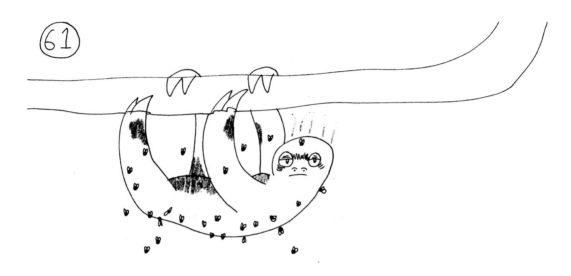

61. Easy Does It

The slow-moving, tree dwelling sloth
Has fur that's like badly-washed cloth
It is really a fact
He grow moss on his back
And he's likely infested with moth.

62. The Wanderer

The albatross flies o'er the ocean
In a kind of perpetual motion
He spends months on end
Away from the land
How he eats and he sleeps, I've no notion.

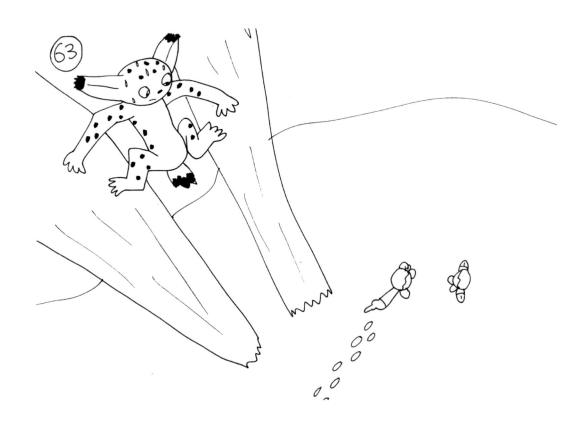

63. Dude of the Wilds

The lynx has fur markings so dapper
With his ear tufts, a real whipper-snapper
It is a great pity
Such a beautiful kitty
Is seen only by hunter and trapper.

64. Live and Learn

The porcupine's quills have been tested
And predators' forays arrested
But the hunting dog's rare
Who takes enough care
To leave this slow poke unmolested.

65

65. Rig a Jig Jig

The whooping cranes' nuptial dance
Is the funniest this side of France
They look like Dutch windmills
With lopsided topsails
Which suddenly started to prance.

66. Fun Fur

The squirrel's tail ends in a whirl
Of beautiful fur in a twirl
Though he's bold and brassy
There is something classy
In the whirl of the twirl of the squirrel.

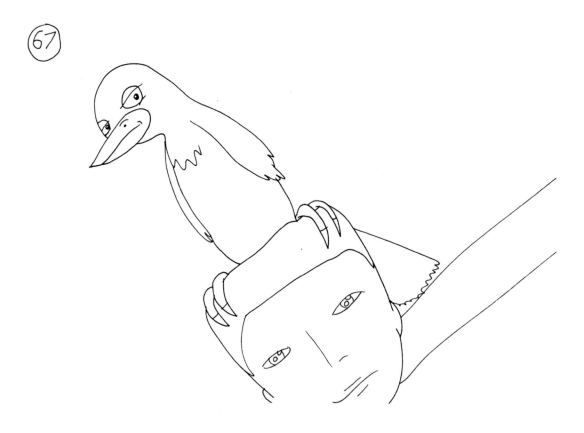

67. Cheese It, E.A. Poe

The raven has much to deplore
In the fate of the long-lost Lenore
This respectable bird
Has not even heard
Of a raven who quoth, " Nevermore."

68. Woo Coo

The chat of the fat turtle dove
Gets boring, when push comes to shove
Though his billing and cooing
And pitching of wooing
Is symbolic of romantic love.

69. Flip Trip

Alone on a hill lived a turtle
Laying eggs that were always infertile
But the hill was so steep
She feared taking the leap
Turning turtle as down she would hurtle.

70. Loan Shark

The white shark with wide gaping jaws
Is a ruffian with many flaws
The human sharks practice
The same business tactics
And bending or breaking of laws.

71. Invidious Comparisons

A moose, with a face like a moose,
Was put down by the Canada goose,
  "So ugly a mug
  Makes you look like a thug
Or a con from the Pen on the loose."

72. Woo Woo

A timber wolf, Lobo by name,
Who thirsted for glory and fame
Got the role of Lothario
On TV Ontario
But was fired, for his wolf call was tame.

73. Tip Top

Mountain goats in their sky-high retreat
Need no shelter from snow, wind and sleet
Can walk along edges
Of high rocky ledges
For they have suction cups on their feet.

74. Die Fledermaus

The squeak of the little brown bat
Gives only a hint where he's at
His comings and goings
And toings and froings
Pursuing mosquito and gnat.

75. Blubber

Harbour seals lying there on the sand
Have no taste for the fat of the land
The fruits of the sea,
Are their cup of tea
The fish is their dish, right at hand.

76. Christmas Travel

Caribou and reindeer are the same
But reindeer don't migrate, are more tame
The travellers' guide
On Santa's sleigh ride
Was a caribou, Rudolph by name.

77. The Grizzly

Beside northwestern mountains and lakes
The grizzly lives, but for short breaks
When he makes a sally
Down this river valley
To load up on fat salmon steaks.

78

78. Night Howl

The lunatic laugh of the loon
Is heard at the rise of the moon
He announces the sight
Of the creatures of night
The owl and the bat and raccoon.

79. It Makes Sense

In fable and song the sly fox
Says "sour grapes" or is put in a box
So one would have thought
There's no reason he's not
Given credit for bagels and lox.

80. What a Comedown

The proud polar bear needs no maps
To hunt seal on polar ice caps
But when the ice goes
And there aren't any floes
He must search around Churchill for scraps.

About the Author

    I. Mary Hackney, was born in Fullarton Township, Perth County, Ontario, Canada. She served in the Canadian Women's Army Corp from 1943 – 1946. Attended Toronto University and University of Ann Arbor in Michigan, obtaining a degree of Doctor of Philosophy (Psychology) in 1958.

    She was Chief Psychologist at Toronto's Hospital For Sick Children in the 1960's and at Women's College in the 1970's and 1980's. She also maintained a private practice, championing children of all ages with special needs.

Mary loved reading and astonished us with her phenomenal memory for reciting reams of poetry. Her creativity showed in her paintings, pottery, gardening and of course limerick writing.

She enjoyed theatre and the arts, and travelled the world, bringing back unusual items to decorate her house. She had a deep appreciation of nature and left a generous endowment to The Escarpment Biosphere Conservancy which protects land and wildlife from Niagara Falls to the tip of Manitoulin Island.

Mary died peacefully in her 93rd year on July 30, 2011. Her spirit remains strong in all of us who knew and loved her.

About the Illustrator

Carly Hatton was diagnosed with high-functioning autism when she was four. Her award-winning art has been displayed and sold throughout Canada, England and the United States.

Her delightful sense of humour is evident in her characters' expressions and antics. She also enjoys making small sculptures and has donated her art to many charities, mainly autism fundraisers, and to senior's organizations for their independent living.

Her drawings have been featured on two book covers regarding autism: "Interactive Play" by Dr. Diana Seach and "Girls Growing Up on the Autism Spectrum" by Dr. Shana Nichols. Carly is one of 54 artists from around the world to have her art displayed in "Artism, The Art of Autism" by Debra Hosseini. Carly's art was also in the first book, "Artism Art by those with Autism" published by Autism Today.

She attends school and when not drawing, writing or enjoying her iPad, she likes to climb trees and spin. She is also very attentive to the two beagles at her house.

Visit Carly at www.CarlysArt.com